ɔn

Discover Your
Destiny

"Eye hath not seen, nor ear heard,
neither have entered into the heart of man,
the things which God hath prepared
for them that love Him."

—1 Corinthians 2:9

Cary Schmidt

Striving Together Publications
4020 E. Lancaster Blvd.
Lancaster, CA 93535
800.201.7748

Cover design by Cary Schmidt and Stephen Houk

Layout by Craig Parker

Editing, proofreading, and assistance by
Amanda Michael and Kayla Nelson

ISBN 1-59894-001-5

Printed in the United States of America

Contents

It's Not Easy Being Dysfunctional

Starting the Journey from a Point of Need

Text

"Remember now thy Creator in the days of thy youth, while the evil days come not, nor the years draw nigh, when thou shalt say, I have no pleasure in them;"—Ecclesiastes 12:1

Overview

This lesson is designed to create an awareness of vulnerability. You must be dependent on God as you enter the adult life for which you are not prepared.

Introduction

_____

_____

_____

I. Congratulations, you're _____

    _____!

    A. _You hate to be thought of as a _____._

    B. _You long to be thought of as an _____._

    C. _You crave _____._

    D. _You are probably _____ about the future._

II. Congratulations, you're _____

    _____!

    A. _You haven't _____ adult _____ before._

    B. _You haven't _____ adult _____ before._

    C. _You could spend the next thirty years_

        _____._

III. Congratulations, you _____!

A. We are all _____.

B. We cannot _____ this journey _____
_____.

C. We must _____ and _____ our
dependence upon _____ and _____.
"But he giveth more grace. Wherefore he saith, God resisteth
the proud, but giveth grace unto the humble."
—JAMES 4:6

"I love them that love me; and those that seek me early shall
find me."—PROVERBS 8:17

"…he is a rewarder of them that diligently seek him."
—HEBREWS 11:6B

D. We must live life by _____.

Conclusion

_____

_____

Study Questions

1. When should you start getting ready for adulthood?

2. What does it mean to be "dysfunctional"?

3. Before God can lead you into his best blessings for your future, what do you need to realize and accept?

4. When it comes to destiny, what are God's "rules"?

5. In what areas of life do you tend to think you're more ready for than you really are?

6. Why do some people get irritated when others try to give them advice about adulthood?

7. How can admitting that you're dysfunctional and that you need God help you today?

8. List three things you can do this week to show God that you are depending upon Him.

Memory Verse

"I love them that love me; and those that seek me early shall find me."—PROVERBS 8:17

Welcome to the "Mistake Zone"

The Ten Most Dangerous Years of Everyone's Life

Text

"Remember now thy Creator in the days of thy youth, while the evil days come not, nor the years draw nigh, when thou shalt say, I have no pleasure in them;"—ECCLESIASTES 12:1

"Blessed is the man that walketh not in the counsel of the ungodly, nor standeth in the way of sinners, nor sitteth in the seat of the scornful. But his delight is in the law of the LORD; and in his law doth he meditate day and night. And he shall be like a tree planted by the rivers of water, that bringeth forth his fruit in his season; his leaf also shall not wither; and whatsoever he doeth shall prosper."—PSALM 1:1–3

"The steps of a good man are ordered by the LORD: and he delighteth in his way."—PSALM 37:23

"A thousand shall fall at thy side, and ten thousand at thy right hand; but it shall not come nigh thee. Only with thine eyes shalt thou behold and see the reward of the wicked. Because thou hast made the LORD, which is my refuge, even the most High, thy habitation;"—PSALM 91:7–9

Overview

The purpose of this lesson is to help you grasp the enormous magnitude of the life-changing decisions you will be required to make in the next ten years.

Introduction

_____

_____

_____

I. Introducing the _____

    A. The "Mistake Zone" encompasses _____
       _____.

    B. The "Mistake Zone" is when life's _____
       _____ will be made.

    C. The "Mistake Zone" is where life's _____
       _____ will be made.

    D. These mistakes have _____
       _____.

II. Understanding "Mistake Zone" _____

_____

_____

    A. These decisions have _____
       _____.

B. You cannot see the _____ of these decisions until _____.

C. None of these decisions will happen by _____, _____, or _____.

"Remember now thy Creator in the days of thy youth, while the evil days come not, nor the years draw nigh, when thou shalt say, I have no pleasure in them;"—ECCLESIASTES 12:1

Conclusion

_____

_____

Study Questions

1. What is the "Mistake Zone"?

2. List several major decisions you will make in the "Mistake Zone."

3. What are some results of making wrong decisions in the "Mistake Zone"?

4. What is God's promise to you during these crucial years of decision-making?

5. Why do you think God allows you to go through the "Mistake Zone"?

6. Why are you not qualified to make these decisions on your own?

7. What kinds of thought patterns, habits, or characteristics can lead someone to making a wrong decision? What can you do to keep yourself from going this same direction?

8. What is the most important principle for you to remember as you go through the "Mistake Zone"?

Memory Verse

"Lead me, O LORD, in thy righteousness because of mine enemies; make thy way straight before my face."—Psalm 5:8

In the Heart of the "Mistake Zone"

Understanding the Risk

Text

"Behold, God is my salvation; I will trust, and not be afraid: for the LORD JEHOVAH is my strength and my song; he also is become my salvation."—ISAIAH 12:2

"For God hath not given us the spirit of fear; but of power, and of love, and of a sound mind."—2 TIMOTHY 1:7

Overview

The purpose of this lesson is to take a closer look at the "Mistake Zone" and to spend time discussing each of the decisions in detail. This will help you grasp the importance of the risks and the importance of making right decisions, the first time around.

Introduction

_____

_____

_____

I. Which _____ will you go to?

A. *It will determine your life* _____.

B. *It will probably determine your life* _____.

C. *It will determine your* _____.

II. Who will you _____?

"Can two walk together, except they be agreed?"—Amos 3:3

"Be ye not unequally yoked together with unbelievers: for what fellowship hath righteousness with unrighteousness? and what communion hath light with darkness?"
—2 Corinthians 6:14

A. *Who you date will determine your*
    _____.

B. *Who you date will determine* _____.

C. *Who you date will greatly* _____ *the condition of your* _____.

III. What will your _____ be?

A. Your first job will determine _____
   _____.

B. Your first job could help you _____.

C. Your first job will reveal your _____
   _____.

IV. What will you _____?

A. How you _____ will reveal your
   _____.

B. How you _____ will reveal your
   _____.

C. How you _____ will reveal
   your _____.

V. Who will be your _____?

A. You will _____
   _____.

B. People will judge you by your _____.

"… for the LORD seeth not as man seeth; for man looketh on the outward appearance, but the LORD looketh on the heart."—1 SAMUEL 16:7

C. Your friends will _____ every part of your life.

VI. What _____ will you choose?

A. The question is not "_____ _____?"

B. The question is "_____ _____?"

C. God's _____ is the only thing that will truly _____.

VII. Who will you _____?

A. A great marriage is _____.

B. A great marriage is _____.

C. Most marriages without God _____.

D. Only God can give you a _____.

VIII.   Where will you _____
_____?

    A.   This will determine where you _____.

    B.   This will determine where your _____
        _____.

    C.   This will determine the _____
        _____.

IX.   What will you _____?

    A.   Will you _____ or _____?

    B.   What does it take to _____
        _____?

    C.   How will you know you're _____
        _____?

X.   When will you have _____
_____?

    A.   When will you have _____?

    B.   _____ will you have?

    C.   How will you _____ them?

D.   What will their _____ be like?

XI.   What _____ will you go to?

   A.   Will you live for God _____?

   B.   What kind of _____?

   C.   Will you lead your family _____?

XII.   Will you maintain _____
   _____?

   A.   Will you stay _____ to God?

   B.   Will you _____ to stay faithful to God?

XIII.   What is your life's _____
   _____?

   A.   Will you live for _____?

   B.   Will you live for _____?

   C.   Will you live for _____?

D. Will you live for _____ and let Him _____?

XIV. What _____ will you live by?

A. Will you _____ your money by _____?

B. Will you _____ God?

C. Will God be able to _____?

"A thousand shall fall at thy side, and ten thousand at thy right hand; but it shall not come nigh thee. Only with thine eyes shalt thou behold and see the reward of the wicked. Because thou hast made the LORD, which is my refuge, even the most High, thy habitation;"
—PSALM 91:7–9

"Behold, God is my salvation; I will trust, and not be afraid: for the LORD JEHOVAH is my strength and my song; he also is become my salvation."—ISAIAH 12:2

Conclusion

_____

_____

Study Questions

1. What will most likely be your first major decision and why is making the right decision so important?

2. Why shouldn't you date a non-Christian?

3. In what ways do friends influence you?

4. What should you look for in a future spouse?

5. Is God more important to you than a paycheck? List some ways you can protect yourself from ever replacing God with a future job.

6. Do you want your life's purpose and mission to be for money, pleasure, possessions, or God? Based on the amount of time you give to each of these in your life right now, which one are you currently living for and what can you do to move forward in the right direction?

7. List some ways that having a car can reflect well or poorly on you.

8. Based on God's promise to you in Psalm 91:7–9, what can you be sure of as you face these decisions?

Memory Verse

"Teach me to do thy will; for thou art my God: thy spirit is good; lead me into the land of uprightness."—PSALM 143:10

Destiny—My Place in the Cosmic Cookie Mix

Understanding Time, Eternity, and Destiny

Text

"Wherefore I put thee in remembrance that thou stir up the gift of God, which is in thee by the putting on of my hands. For God hath not given us the spirit of fear; but of power, and of love, and of a sound mind. Be not thou therefore ashamed of the testimony of our Lord, nor of me his prisoner: but be thou partaker of the afflictions of the gospel according to the power of God; Who hath saved us, and called us with an holy calling, not according to our works, but according to his own purpose and grace, which was given us in Christ Jesus before the world began,"—2 TIMOTHY 1:6–9

"Before I formed thee in the belly I knew thee; and before thou camest forth out of the womb I sanctified thee, and I ordained thee a prophet unto the nations."—JEREMIAH 1:5

"For I know the thoughts that I think toward you, saith the LORD, thoughts of peace, and not of evil, to give you an expected end."—JEREMIAH 29:11

Overview

The purpose of this lesson is to help you understand God's eternal plan for your life as conceived before the world began. You are not an accident but a masterful design of the Heavenly Father, and you have a divine mission to fulfill for eternity.

Introduction

_____

_____

_____

I.   The way it _____

A.   _Evolution is _____._

B.   _The universe shows _____
       _____._

C.   _No _____ shows animals crossing
       species and producing fertile offspring._

D.   _Evolution is not _____, which
       means it is not _____._

E.   _History, science, and archeology all support
       the _____._

F.   _Evolution is a religion of _____;
       Creation is a religion of _____._

G.   _The fossil record supports _____
       _____._

II. The way it _____ and
_____

"The heavens declare the glory of God; and the firmament sheweth his handywork"—Psalm 19:1

    A.   God created _____.

    B.   God has an _____
        for everything He created.

    C.   Your _____ about Creation will
        determine your _____.

    D.   You are not an _____.

    E.   You have an _____.

III. The beginning of _____

"Who hath saved us, and called us with an holy calling, not according to our works, but according to his own purpose and grace, which was given us in Christ Jesus before the world began,"—2 Timothy 1:9

    A.   God has an _____
        that's bigger than _____.

"Blessed be the God and Father of our Lord Jesus Christ, who hath blessed us with all spiritual blessings in heavenly places in Christ: According as he hath chosen us in him before the foundation of the world, that we should be holy and without blame before him in love: Having

predestinated us unto the adoption of children by Jesus Christ to himself, according to the good pleasure of his will, To the praise of the glory of his grace, wherein he hath made us accepted in the beloved. In whom we have redemption through his blood, the forgiveness of sins, according to the riches of his grace; Wherein he hath abounded toward us in all wisdom and prudence; Having made known unto us the mystery of his will, according to his good pleasure which he hath purposed in himself: That in the dispensation of the fullness of times he might gather together in one all things in Christ, both which are in heaven, and which are on earth; even in him: In whom also we have obtained an inheritance, being predestinated according to the purpose of him who worketh all things after the counsel of his own will: That we should be to the praise of his glory, who first trusted in Christ."—Ephesians 1:3–12

   B.   God made you to _____ an eternal purpose.

   C.   God _____ your purpose before He _____.

IV. _____ destiny

   A.   Your destiny is _____.

   B.   Your destiny is _____!

C. You will only be _____ as you
    _____ your destiny.

D. Your destiny will give you a _____
    _____.

E. Your destiny represents _____.

F. Your destiny can be _____.

G. Your destiny is _____.

H. Your destiny arrives from _____, by _____,
    on a _____.

I.   Your destiny is a _____.
"Before I formed thee in the belly I knew thee; and before
thou camest forth out of the womb I sanctified thee..."
—JEREMIAH 1:5

Conclusion

_____
_____

Study Questions

1. What are some of the problems with the theory of evolution?

2. How does what you believe about Creation affect your future?

3. Why did God create you?

4. What is "destiny"?

5. List several reasons a person might choose to believe evolution.

6. List several reasons we know Creation is true.

7. Why do you think God would create a destiny specifically for you?

8. Fulfilling your destiny is the only way you will ever be truly happy. Why?

Memory Verse

"Before I formed thee in the belly I knew thee; and before thou camest forth out of the womb I sanctified thee, and I ordained thee a prophet unto the nations."—JEREMIAH 1:5

Destiny Shmestiny…
I Have Plans, Man!

Understanding How Your Plans Mesh with
God's Eternal Purpose

Text

"I beseech you therefore, brethren, by the mercies of God, that ye present your bodies a living sacrifice, holy, acceptable unto God, which is your reasonable service. And be not conformed to this world: but be ye transformed by the renewing of your mind, that ye may prove what is that good, and acceptable, and perfect, will of God."—ROMANS 12:1–2

"Delight thyself also in the LORD; and he shall give thee the desires of thine heart."—PSALM 37:4

"He will fulfil the desire of them that fear him: he also will hear their cry, and will save them."—PSALM 145:19

Overview

The purpose of this lesson is to encourage you to put your well-laid plans on hold long enough to hear this series and consider its profound relevance to your life. You may be listening to this series but dismissing it because you've already made your plans. Set those plans aside and give God a chance to teach you something new.

Introduction

_____

_____

_____

I. The truth about _____

A. *God creates all of us with* _____
_____.

B. *Often our abilities, gifts, and desires become
our* _____, *rather than God.*

"Wherefore, my dearly beloved, flee from idolatry."
—1 Corinthians 10:14

*"Nevertheless I have somewhat against thee, because thou
hast left thy first love."*—Revelation 2:4

C. *Finding God's plan begins with* _____
_____.

D. *God has* _____ *for you
than you can possibly* _____.

II. The truth about "_____"

A. *Only God can* _____ *if your
plans are truly right for* _____.

B. *If you* _____ *your plans over
God, you will never* _____.

C. Your plans could be _____.

D. God could _____ your plans and dreams if He wants to.

E. God could give you _____.

F. Even _____ desires can become _____.

G. Gifts and abilities should be _____ but not _____ in place of God.

III. _____ or _____—what will it be?

A. _____ set His will aside to follow _____.

B. Even _____ desires can sidetrack you from God's _____ desires.

C. Your will must be _____ so that you can find God's.

D. Misery is doing _____ but never _____.

"He will fulfil the desire of them that fear him: he also will hear their cry, and will save them."—PSALM 145:19

Conclusion

_____

_____

_____

Study Questions

1. What is the first step to finding God's plan for your life?

2. List three of the "truths" about your plans that you, personally, need to remember the most.

3. How can good desires become idols?

4. What is a sure way to making yourself miserable in the future?

5. What is the difference between deciding to do something "for God" and doing "whatever God leads"?

6.   What are some dangers of following your own plans?

7.   Write down one gift or ability that God has given you and describe how it can be abused and how it can be developed.

8.   Even Jesus put His will aside for God's will. Describe one event in the Bible when Jesus did this and how it affected His life and the lives of those around Him.

Memory Verse

"He that trusteth in his own heart is a fool: but whoso walketh wisely, he shall be delivered."—PROVERBS 28:26

It's Time to Get Serious

Tool #1 for Right Decision-Making—A Serious Mind

Text

"When I was a child, I spake as a child, I understood as a child, I thought as a child: but when I became a man, I put away childish things."—1 CORINTHIANS 13:11

"Wherefore gird up the loins of your mind, be sober, and hope to the end for the grace that is to be brought unto you at the revelation of Jesus Christ;"—1 PETER 1:13

"The aged women likewise, that they be in behaviour as becometh holiness, not false accusers, not given to much wine, teachers of good things; That they may teach the young women to be sober, to love their husbands, to love their children, To be discreet, chaste, keepers at home, good, obedient to their own husbands, that the word of God be not blasphemed. Young men likewise exhort to be sober minded. In all things shewing thyself a pattern of good works: in doctrine shewing uncorruptness, gravity, sincerity,"—TITUS 2:3–7

"Be sober, be vigilant; because your adversary the devil, as a roaring lion, walketh about, seeking whom he may devour:"—1 PETER 5:8

Overview

The purpose of this lesson is to emphasize a sober mind and to challenge you to begin very seriously and deliberately pursuing God's will for your future.

Introduction

_____

_____

_____

*"When I was a child, I spake as a child, I understood as a child,
I thought as a child: but when I became a man, I put away
childish things."*—1 CORINTHIANS 13:11

I.   Being serious does not _____.

*"The aged women likewise, that they be in behaviour as
becometh holiness, not false accusers, not given to much wine,
teachers of good things; That they may teach the young women
to be sober, to love their husbands, to love their children, To be
discreet, chaste, keepers at home, good, obedient to their own
husbands, that the word of God be not blasphemed. Young men
likewise exhort to be sober minded. In all things shewing thyself
a pattern of good works: in doctrine shewing uncorruptness,
gravity, sincerity,"*—TITUS 2:3–7

    A.   *Your authorities are commanded to _____
_____ about being serious.*

    B.   *You are commanded to _____ about
being serious.*

    C.   *Developing a serious mind will be _____
_____.*

II. _____ of your mind.

"Wherefore gird up the loins of your mind, be sober, and hope to the end for the grace that is to be brought unto you at the revelation of Jesus Christ;"—1 PETER 1:13

    A.   *What is _____?*

    B.   *_____ gird up the loins?*

    C.   *Use your sober mind to _____.*

    D.   *Use your sober mind to _____.*

    E.   *Use your sober mind to _____*
       _____.

III. _____ of your enemy.

"Be sober, be vigilant; because your adversary the devil, as a roaring lion, walketh about, seeking whom he may devour:"
—1 PETER 5:8

    A.   *You are the _____ of a _____.*

    B.   *You are the _____ of a _____*
       _____.

    C.   *You must choose to _____*
       and _____.

"Therefore let us not sleep, as do others; but let us watch and be sober."—1 Thessalonians 5:6

"But while men slept, his enemy came..."—Matthew 13:25a

Conclusion

_____

_____

Study Questions

1. What is "tool #1" for making right decisions?

2. What does it mean to be sober minded?

3. Why is it important that you "gird up the loins of your mind"?

4. To avoid your enemy, what must you do?

5. What lessons have you learned recently that have taught you the importance of being serious?

6. List several examples of how to "gird up the loins of your mind."

7. What can happen to a person who never learns to be serious?

8. Maturity is the acceptance of responsibility. What are some things you can do this week to help you grow in maturity?

Memory Verse

"Therefore let us not sleep, as do others; but let us watch and be sober."—1 Thessalonians 5:6

If You Are Among the Very "Pure" in Heart

Tool #2 for Right Decision-Making—a Pure Heart

Text

"Blessed are the pure in heart: for they shall see God."
—MATTHEW 5:8

"Keep thy heart with all diligence; for out of it are the issues of life."—PROVERBS 4:23

Overview

The purpose of this lesson is to help you understand the role that your heart plays in the decision-making process and to emphasize the priority of keeping your heart pure so that right decisions can be clearly seen.

Introduction

_____

_____

_____

I. What is a _____?

"Keep thy heart with all diligence; for out of it are the issues of life."—PROVERBS 4:23

    A. *Your heart _____ life's _____ (feeler).*

    B. *Your heart _____ life's _____ (wanter).*

    C. *Your heart _____ life's _____ (chooser).*

    D. *Your heart _____ your _____ (thinker).*

II. Your heart is what God _____ _____.

"But the LORD said unto Samuel, Look not on his countenance, or on the height of his stature; because I have refused him: for the LORD seeth not as man seeth; for man looketh on the outward appearance, but the LORD looketh on the heart."
—I SAMUEL 16:7

    A. *Man sees the _____.*
    "A good name is rather to be chosen than great riches, and loving favour rather than silver and gold."—PROVERBS 22:1

"This people draweth nigh unto me with their mouth, and honoureth me with their lips; but their heart is far from me."—MATTHEW 15:8

    B.   God sees the _____.

    C.   God cares about both the _____
        _____.

    D.   God desires _____ to
        produce _____ to Christ.

III. Your heart can guide you _____ God's will.

    A.   Your heart can be _____.

    B.   _____ hearts make _____.

    C.   Your heart is the _____ through which
        you will _____.

IV. Your heart can guide you _____ God's will.

"Blessed are the pure in heart: for they shall see God."
—MATTHEW 5:8

    A.   Your heart can be _____.

    B.   Pure hearts _____.

C. Pure hearts _____.

D. Pure hearts _____.

V. Your heart must be _____.

A. A _____ creates a dirty heart.

B. _____ creates a dirty heart.

C. A dirty heart cannot make _____.

D. A pure heart must be _____.

"If we confess our sins, he is faithful and just to forgive us our sins, and to cleanse us from all unrighteousness."
—1 John 1:9

VI. How to have a _____.

"Wherewithal shall a young man cleanse his way? by taking heed thereto according to thy word."—Psalm 119:9

"Have mercy upon me, O God, according to thy lovingkindness: according unto the multitude of thy tender mercies blot out my transgressions. Wash me thoroughly from mine iniquity, and cleanse me from my sin. For I acknowledge my transgressions: and my sin is ever before me. Against thee, thee only, have I sinned, and done this evil in thy sight:"— Psalm 51:1–4

A. A pure heart _____.

B. A pure heart _____.

C. A pure heart _____.

D. A pure heart _____.

E. A pure heart _____.

VII. Your heart can be _____.

"But now, O LORD, thou art our father; we are the clay, and thou our potter; and we all are the work of thy hand."
—Isaiah 64:8

"O house of Israel, cannot I do with you as this potter? saith the LORD. Behold, as the clay is in the potter's hand, so are ye in mine hand, O house of Israel."—Jeremiah 18:6

"A new heart also will I give you, and a new spirit will I put within you: and I will take away the stony heart out of your flesh, and I will give you an heart of flesh."—Ezekiel 36:26

A. A pure heart is like _____.

B. _____ can be changed by God.
"Blessed are the pure in heart: for they shall see God."
—Matthew 5:8

Conclusion

_____

_____

Study Questions

1. In what four ways does your spiritual heart function in your life?

2. What are the dangers of having an impure heart?

3. List four characteristics of a pure heart.

4. What is God's promise to you if you keep your heart pure?

5. How does a pure heart guide you into God's will?

6. Why is it important that you care for both your outward appearance and your inward heart?

7. If your heart is the lens through which you will make major decisions, what are some simple habits you can start developing right now in order to cleanse your heart every day?

8. What are some thoughts, feelings, or desires that you would like God to change, and what do you need to do in these areas to allow God to begin molding your heart?

Memory Verse

"Wherewithal shall a young man cleanse his way? by taking heed thereto according to thy word."—PSALM 119:9

I Don't Want to Grow Up—I'm a Toys R Us Kid!

Tool #3 for Right Decision-Making —a Courageous Spirit

Text

"Be strong and of a good courage: for unto this people shalt thou divide for an inheritance the land, which I sware unto their fathers to give them."—JOSHUA 1:6

"Whosoever he be that doth rebel against thy commandment, and will not hearken unto thy words in all that thou commandest him, he shall be put to death: only be strong and of a good courage."—JOSHUA 1:18

"Finally, my brethren, be strong in the Lord, and in the power of his might."—EPHESIANS 6:10

Overview

The purpose of this lesson is to encourage you to claim God's strength and to courageously press forward into adulthood, in spite of the intimidating odds. Your enemy wants you to be afraid. God wants you to be courageous!

Introduction

_____
_____
_____

I. Choose to _____ in life.

A. *Most young adults _____.*

B. *Most young adults _____.*

C. *Many young adults _____*
    as long as possible.

D. *God _____ to _____*
    _____ in life.

II. Avoid _____ into life.

A. *You cannot decide "_____."*

B. *The choice "_____" is a choice*
    "_____."

C. *Build your life on _____, not on*
    _____.

D. *Realize _____ the*
    decision-making process.

III. Be _____ and _____.

   A.   *God called Joshua _____.*

   B.   *_____ tempted Joshua to _____.*

   C.   *Joshua chose _____ and _____.*

   D.   *You must choose to either _____*
      or _____.

IV. There are _____ of a

_____.

   A.   _____

   B.   _____

   C.   _____

   D.   _____

   E.   _____

"For God hath not given us the spirit of fear; but of power, and of love, and of a sound mind."— 2 TIMOTHY 1:7

"Finally, my brethren, be strong in the Lord, and in the power of his might."—EPHESIANS 6:10

Conclusion

_____

_____

_____

Study Questions

1. Why are most young adults afraid of growing up?

2. In deciding "not to decide," you are actually making what decision?

3. What is the only way to move forward in life?

4. What are the five enemies of your future? Give a short description of how each of these can keep you from moving forward and living out God's will for your life.

5. What scares you the most about "growing up"?

6. The transition between childhood and adulthood is very much a proving time. In ten or fifteen years, what would you like to be able to say about this time in your life?

7. Of the five enemies of the future, which one do you struggle with the most? What can you do to overcome this?

8. Write one decision you have made as a result of this lesson, and outline your "plan of attack" to see this decision through.

Memory Verse

"For God hath not given us the spirit of fear; but of power, and of love, and of a sound mind."—2 TIMOTHY 1:7

Hey, Buddy, You've Got Boardwalk!!

Tool #4 for Right Decision-Making—God's Wisdom

Text

*"If any of you lack wisdom, let him ask of God, that giveth to all
men liberally, and upbraideth not; and it shall be given him."*
—JAMES 1:5

*"For my thoughts are not your thoughts, neither are your ways
my ways, saith the LORD. For as the heavens are higher than
the earth, so are my ways higher than your ways, and my
thoughts than your thoughts."*—ISAIAH 55:8–9

*"For this cause we also, since the day we heard it, do not
cease to pray for you, and to desire that ye might be filled
with the knowledge of his will in all wisdom and spiritual
understanding;"*—COLOSSIANS 1:9

Overview

The purpose of this lesson is to explain the vital role that
wisdom plays in the decision-making process and to commit
you to asking God for wisdom on a daily basis.

Introduction

_____

_____

_____

I. The _wisdom_ of God—"what God sees"

*"For my thoughts are not your thoughts, neither are your ways
my ways, saith the LORD. For as the heavens are higher than
the earth, so are my ways higher than your ways, and my
thoughts than your thoughts."*—Isaiah 55:8–9

*"O the depth of the riches both of the wisdom and knowledge of
God! how unsearchable are his judgments, and his ways past
finding out!"*—Romans 11:33

    A.   God sees _____ you cannot see.

    B.   God sees _____ you cannot see.

    C.   God understands a _____ you don't
        understand.

    D.   God offers to let you _____ and _____
        what He _____ and _____.

II. The _____ for your future decisions

*"For this cause we…do not cease to pray for you, and to desire
that ye might be filled with the knowledge of his will in all
wisdom and spiritual understanding;"*—Colossians 1:9

"Then said I, Wisdom is better than strength:"
—ECCLESIASTES 9:16A

"Wisdom is better than weapons of war:"
—ECCLESIASTES 9:18A

"Wisdom strengtheneth the wise more than ten mighty men which are in the city."—ECCLESIASTES 7:19

"Through wisdom is an house builded; and by understanding it is established:"—PROVERBS 24:3

"He that getteth wisdom loveth his own soul: he that keepeth understanding shall find good."—PROVERBS 19:8

"How much better is it to get wisdom than gold! and to get understanding rather to be chosen than silver!"
—PROVERBS 16:16

"The lips of the righteous feed many: but fools die for want of wisdom."—PROVERBS 10:21

"Get wisdom, get understanding: forget it not; neither decline from the words of my mouth."—PROVERBS 4:5

"Wisdom is the principal thing; therefore get wisdom: and with all thy getting get understanding."—PROVERBS 4:7

"The fear of the LORD is the beginning of knowledge: but fools despise wisdom and instruction."—PROVERBS 1:7

A. _____ because they don't have it.

B. Wisdom is better than _____.

C. Following godly wisdom brings _____.

III. _____ wisdom from God

A. True wisdom comes _____.

"Who is a wise man and endued with knowledge among you? let him shew out of a good conversation his works with meekness of wisdom. But if ye have bitter envying and strife in your hearts, glory not, and lie not against the truth. This wisdom descendeth not from above, but is earthly, sensual, devilish. For where envying and strife is, there is confusion and every evil work. But the wisdom that is from above is first pure, then peaceable, gentle, and easy to be intreated, full of mercy and good fruits, without partiality, and without hypocrisy."—JAMES 3:13–17

"Where is the wise? where is the scribe? where is the disputer of this world? hath not God made foolish the wisdom of this world? For after that in the wisdom of God the world by wisdom knew not God, it pleased God by the foolishness of preaching to save them that believe. For the Jews require a sign, and the Greeks seek after wisdom: But we preach Christ crucified, unto the Jews a stumblingblock, and unto the Greeks foolishness; But unto them which are called, both Jews and Greeks, Christ the power of God, and the wisdom of God."—I CORINTHIANS 1:20–24

B. Godly wisdom experiences _____.

"But the natural man receiveth not the things of the Spirit of God: for they are foolishness unto him: neither can he know them, because they are spiritually discerned."
—I CORINTHIANS 2:14

C.   Godly wisdom is more valuable than _____

_____.

"Wisdom is the principal thing; therefore get wisdom: and with all thy getting get understanding."—PROVERBS 4:7

"Let this mind be in you, which was also in Christ Jesus:"—PHILIPPIANS 2:5

D.   Godly wisdom is _gained by asking_.

"If any of you lack wisdom, let him ask of God, that giveth to all men liberally, and upbraideth not; and it shall be given him."—JAMES 1:5

E.   God blesses those who _ask for wisdom_.

"And now, O LORD my God, thou hast made thy servant king instead of David my father: and I am but a little child: I know not how to go out or come in. And thy servant is in the midst of thy people which thou hast chosen, a great people, that cannot be numbered nor counted for multitude. Give therefore thy servant an understanding heart to judge thy people, that I may discern between good and bad: for who is able to judge this thy so great a people? And the speech pleased the Lord, that Solomon had asked this thing. And God said unto him," *"Because thou hast asked this thing, and hast not asked for thyself long life; neither hast asked riches for thyself, nor hast asked the life of thine enemies; but hast asked for thyself understanding to discern judgment; Behold, I have done according to thy words: lo, I have given thee a wise and an understanding heart; so that there was none like thee before thee, neither after thee shall any arise like unto thee. And I have also given thee that which thou hast not*

asked, both riches, and honour: so that there shall not be any among the kings like unto thee all thy days. And if thou wilt walk in my ways, to keep my statutes and my commandments, as thy father David did walk, then I will lengthen thy days."—1 KINGS 3:7–14

F.   You'll never _Feel like you have wisdom_____.
"And Jesus increased in wisdom and stature, and in favour with God and man."—LUKE 2:52

"Let the word of Christ dwell in you richly in all wisdom,"
—COLOSSIANS 3:16A

"Wisdom is the principal thing,"—PROVERBS 4:7A

Conclusion

_____ N._____

_____

Wisdom

Study Questions

1. What is godly wisdom?

   Spirtual understanding, seeing thing the way god sees them.

2. What two things does God see in your future that you cannot see? *dangers and blessings*

3. What kind of people succeed and why?

   People seeing thing how they really are—godly wisdom

4. How do you gain godly wisdom?

   By asking for it.

5. Why is it so important that you ask God for wisdom every day? *So you'll never feel like you have wisdom*

6. Think about a decision you made in the past that you regret because you didn't ask God for wisdom. Describe this event and how the consequences might have been different if you had God's wisdom on the matter. *i was in a fight with my sister about something she thought was wrong but i thought was right. and it turned out to be right.*

7. Godly wisdom is more valuable than higher education. Why? *knowledge makes you smart, but not wise.*

8. Why should you start daily seeking God's wisdom now, instead of waiting until you have big decisions to make? *the most valueble resource.*

Memory Verse

"Wisdom is the principal thing; therefore get wisdom: and with all thy getting get understanding."—PROVERBS 4:7

Believing is Seeing

Tool #5 for Right Decision-Making—A Life of Faith

Text

*"Now faith is the substance of things hoped for, the evidence
of things not seen. For by it the elders obtained a good report.
Through faith we understand that the worlds were framed by
the word of God, so that things which are seen were not made
of things which do appear. By faith Abel offered unto God
a more excellent sacrifice than Cain, by which he obtained
witness that he was righteous, God testifying of his gifts: and
by it he being dead yet speaketh. By faith Enoch was translated
that he should not see death; and was not found, because
God had translated him: for before his translation he had
this testimony, that he pleased God. But without faith it is
impossible to please him: for he that cometh to God must
believe that he is, and that he is a rewarder of them that
diligently seek him."*—HEBREWS 11:1–6

Overview

The purpose of this lesson is to help you understand the role
that faith plays in the Christian life and in the process of
making right decisions. You will be challenged to step out
in obedience to God, even when the circumstances don't
seem to make sense to human reasoning.

Introduction

_____

_____

_____

I. God relates to us _By Faith_.

"Now faith is the substance of things hoped for, the evidence of things not seen."—HEBREWS 11:1

    A. People say, "_Show me and i'll Belive_."

    B. God says, "_Belive me and i'll Show You_."

    C. Faith doesn't work by _Sight_.

    D. Faith doesn't work by _Sense_.

    "O taste and see that the LORD is good: blessed is the man that trusteth in him."—PSALM 34:8

    "The LORD redeemeth the soul of his servants: and none of them that trust in him shall be desolate."—PSALM 34:22

II. Why did God _Choose Faith_?

    A. God could have chosen to relate to us by _Sight_.

B. God purposefully designed to __hide himself__
    and to relate to us by faith.

*"That in the dispensation of the fulness of times he might
gather together in one all things in Christ, both which are
in heaven, and which are on earth; even in him: In whom
also we have obtained an inheritance, being predestinated
according to the purpose of him who worketh all things
after the counsel of his own will: That we should be to the
praise of his glory, who first trusted in Christ."*
—Ephesians 1:10–12

C. God gives us __intelligent__ faith, not
    __Blind__ faith.

D. God __proves__ our faith after it is expressed.
"Know ye not that we shall judge angels?"
—1 Corinthians 6:3

E. Our faith __fulfills__ God's eternal purpose.

III. What is __Faith__ ?

*"Behold, the handmaid of the Lord; be it unto me according to
thy word."*—Luke 1:38

"For now we see through a glass, darkly; but then face to face:"
—1 Corinthians 13:12A

A. Faith is __not a force__ .

B. Faith is simply __trusting god__ .

C. Faith _opposes human reasoning_ .

D. Faith requires circumstances that _do not make sense_ .

E. Faith is always _rewarded by god_ .

IV. How does God _Respond_ to faith?

"But without faith it is impossible to please him: for he that cometh to God must believe that he is, and that he is a rewarder of them that diligently seek him."—HEBREWS 11:6

A. Faith greatly _Pleases_ and _delights_ God.

B. Faith _moves_ God _into action_ in our lives.

C. Faith _allows_ God to _do the imposible_ .

D. Faith always brings _gods best rewards_ .

"...I being in the way, the LORD led me..."
—GENESIS 24:27B

Conclusion

_____

_____

Study Questions

1. What is the difference between God's view and people's view of faith? *we do his will and see the results*

2. Why did God choose faith as a means of relating to us?
   it fufills god's eternal purpose.

3. Based on the information given in this lesson, what is faith? *to trust god without seeing him.*

4. What happens when we exercise faith in our lives?
   we see god at work. he rewards and enables

5. Thinking about your own future, describe how your actions and thinking might be different if you lived by sight and if you lived by faith.
   i would be self centered, worried

6. Compare and contrast intelligent faith with blind faith.

intelligent faith is if there is evidence for your faith.

blind faith is no evidence.

7. In what area of your life right now do you struggle with the most when it comes to having faith in God? Why should you trust Him in this area?

8. List three examples in the Bible of how God blessed someone because they had faith.

M,s,i, ruth, abraham

Memory Verse

"O taste and see that the LORD is good: blessed is the man that trusteth in him."—PSALM 34:8

Only Weird People Wear Their Pants Backwards

*Step #1 for Right Decision-Making
—Refuse To Trust Yourself*

Text

"Trust in the LORD with all thine heart; and lean not unto thine own understanding. In all thy ways acknowledge him, and he shall direct thy paths."—PROVERBS 3:5–6

Overview

The purpose of this lesson is to challenge you to place your full 100% trust in God, and to be wary of your own understanding or perspective.

Introduction

_____

_____

_____

I. **The problem with** _Self trust_

    A. *We cannot* _see what god sees_ .

    B. *We do not* _know what the future holds_

    C. *We are* _prone to be wrong_ .

    D. *Trusting self* _directly defies god_ .

II. _refusing_ **to trust yourself**

"Trust in the Lord with all thine heart; and lean not unto thine own understanding. In all thy ways acknowledge Him and He shall direct thy paths."—PROVERBS 3:5–6

    A. *People who make right decisions* _do not trust themself_ .

    B. *People who make right decisions* _reconize there own weakness_ .

    C. *People who make right decisions* _choose to trust god fully_ .

emotions make terrible guides

III. The _Subtle Power_ of self-deception

A. It is natural to _lean to own under standing_.

B. It is possible to _decieve ourselves_ away from _____.

C. We must _respect emotions_ and _____.

*"I am crucified with Christ: nevertheless I live; yet not I, but Christ liveth in me: and the life which I now live in the flesh I live by the faith of the Son of God, who loved me, and gave himself for me."—*GALATIANS 2:20

*"For if our heart condemn us, God is greater than our heart, and knoweth all things."—*I JOHN 3:20

D. _feelings_ will always follow _obedience_ to God.

feelings will always follow obedience

IV. Putting your _trust to the test_

A. Write out your _future dreams and plans_ on a blank sheet of paper.

B. _Dream big_ and be specific.

C. Get a big red marker and write "_do not trust this_" across the top.

D. Hang it in a _Prominent_ place.

"Whether therefore ye eat, or drink, or whatsoever ye do, do all to the glory of God."—1 CORINTHIANS 10:31

"Thou wilt keep him in perfect peace, whose mind is stayed on thee: because he trusteth in thee."—ISAIAH 26:3

Conclusion

_____

_____

Study Questions

1. What are some problems with trusting self?

   You put yourself in a "hole"
   We don't know what the future holds
   We are prone to be wrong
   it directly defies god

2. List the three characteristics of people who make right decisions.

   they don't trust themselves, they recognize their own weaknesses

3. How can you deceive yourself?

   by leaning on your own understanding

4. What can keep you from trusting the guidance of God's Word?

   trusting ourselves. Following our emotions

5. Why is trusting yourself directly defiant towards God?

   Your focused on yourself and not god

---

6. Describe some of your own weaknesses and why it is important that you trust God with them.

   Im to shy and soft spoken at school and i thin its imporant so we know how to trust them

7. How can emotions deceive you?

   If you feel wrong, you do wrong.

8. On a separate sheet of paper, follow the steps listed under "Putting your trust to the test" in the lesson outline.

Memory Verse

"Thou wilt keep him in perfect peace, whose mind is stayed on thee: because he trusteth in thee."—ISAIAH 26:3

Dimples, Donuts, and Destiny

Step #2—Seek and Surrender to God's Will

Text

"But seek ye first the kingdom of God, and his righteousness; and all these things shall be added unto you."—MATTHEW 6:33

"I beseech you therefore, brethren, by the mercies of God, that ye present your bodies a living sacrifice, holy, acceptable unto God, which is your reasonable service. And be not conformed to this world: but be ye transformed by the renewing of your mind, that ye may prove what is that good, and acceptable, and perfect, will of God."—ROMANS 12:1–2

"Thus saith the LORD, the God of Israel; Like these good figs, so will I acknowledge them that are carried away captive of Judah, whom I have sent out of this place into the land of the Chaldeans for their good. For I will set mine eyes upon them for good, and I will bring them again to this land: and I will build them, and not pull them down; and I will plant them, and not pluck them up. And I will give them an heart to know me, that I am the LORD: and they shall be my people, and I will be their God: for they shall return unto me with their whole heart."—JEREMIAH 24:5–7

Overview

This lesson is designed to encourage you to seek God's perfect will above all other earthly pursuits, and to surrender to it completely before you know what it is.

Introduction

_____

_____

_____

I. Why do some people _trust_ God's will?

A. It is _Vauqe_ .

B. It seems to be a _threat_ to your dreams.

C. It can be a _Frustating quest_ .

D. We do not understand how _good_ God's plans are.

II. What is _God's will_ ?

"Thus saith the LORD, the God of Israel; Like these good figs, so will I acknowledge them that are carried away captive of Judah, whom I have sent out of this place into the land of the Chaldeans for their good. For I will set mine eyes upon them for good, and I will bring them again to this land: and I will build them, and not pull them down; and I will plant them, and not pluck them up. And I will give them an heart to know me, that I am the LORD: and they shall be my people, and I will be their God: for they shall return unto me with their whole heart."—JEREMIAH 24:5–7

"Thou wilt shew me the path of life: in thy presence is fulness of joy; at thy right hand there are pleasures for evermore."
—PSALM 16:11

A.   God's will is _good_.

B.   God's will is His plan _to bless you_.

C.   God's will is His plan _to lead you_ and _guide you_ in life.

"For God hath not given us the spirit of fear; but of power, and of love, and of a sound mind."—2 TIMOTHY 1:7

D.   God's will is His plan _provide for you_.

E.   God's will is His plan _to give you true success_.

F.   God's will is never _painless or problem free_.

G.   God's will is never _effortless or easy_.

H.   God's will is the _only path_ to full and abundant _joy_ in life.

I.   God's will brings _purpose_ to every _trial_ in your life.

J.   God's will brings _provision_ to every _need_ in your life.

K.   God's will is the _only path_ to a life with _no regrets_.

III. How does God _reveal_ His will?

A. God _Always_ reveals His will.

B. God reveals His will in _Bite Size Peices_.

C. God reveals His will _By faith_.

D. God only leads those with _Willing hearts_

E. God promises to _lead you_ into His will.

F. God's _Condition_ is that you must be _leadable_.

G. If you are _leadable_, God promises to _guide you_.

IV. _Seek_ God's will first.

A. God _Comands_ you to seek Him.

B. God _rewards_ those who seek Him.

C. God _leads_ those who seek Him.

D. God is _Pleased_ by those who seek Him.

E. Seeking God's will means _god is Your 1st priority_.

V. ___how___ should a person seek God?

   A. _read, study, medistate_ on the Bible.

   B. Walk with God in ___Prayer___.

   C. Make ___Church___ a priority.

   D. Read good ___book and biographies___.

   E. Listen to ___Godly music___.

   F. Deliberately _Seperate from worldy influences._

VI. _Surrender_ **to God's will** _Completely_.

   A. You must choose _____
before you _____.

   B. God will _____ His will to those
who _____.

   C. _____ surrender to God's will is
_____.

"I beseech you therefore, brethren, by the mercies of
God, that ye present your bodies a living sacrifice, holy,
acceptable unto God, which is your reasonable service. And
be not conformed to this world: but be ye transformed by
the renewing of your mind, that ye may prove what is that

good, and acceptable, and perfect, will of God."
—Romans 12:1–2

"Blessed is every one that feareth the LORD; that walketh in his ways."—Psalm 128:1

Conclusion

_____

_____

Study Questions

1.   Why do some people resist God's will?

2.   How does God reveal His will?

3.   How does God respond towards those who seek Him?

4.   What is reasonable Christianity?

5.   List some promises of doing God's will that you hope to see fulfilled in your own life.

6. Describe some of the struggles you may face if you choose God's will, but explain why the struggles would be worth it.

7. What does it mean to be "lead-able," and how can you become a more "lead-able" person?

8. What are you currently doing to seek God? Name one other thing that you will do this week to help you seek God.

Memory Verse

"Blessed is every one that feareth the LORD; that walketh in his ways."—PSALM 128:1

Speak Up, God, I Can't Hear You!

Step #3—Pray About Your Decision

Text

"Pray without ceasing."—I THESSALONIANS 5:17

"The wicked, through the pride of his countenance, will not seek after God: God is not in all his thoughts."—PSALM 10:4

"For God speaketh once, yea twice, yet man perceiveth it not."—JOB 33:14

"And the LORD called Samuel again the third time. And he arose and went to Eli, and said, Here am I; for thou didst call me. And Eli perceived that the LORD had called the child."—I SAMUEL 3:8

Overview

The purpose of this lesson is to help you understand how God speaks to you and the part that prayer plays in your decision-making process. In this lesson, you will understand that God speaks with a still, small voice, and He must be carefully sought out and listened to. You will be challenged to silence the other voices in your world so that you can hear and follow God's voice alone.

Introduction

S

I. Silencing the _Voices From Without_

A. We are all faced with many _oppurtunities_ in life.

B. Each opportunity could potentially _Draw us away From God's will_.

C. The voices of these opportunities must be _Silenced or Surrender_.

D. If we listen to the voices of _Selfish oppurtunities_ we cannot _hears god voice_.

II. Understanding how God _Speaks to his Children_

"And he came thither unto a cave, and lodged there; and, behold, the word of the LORD came to him, and he said unto him, What doest thou here, Elijah? And he said, I have been very jealous for the LORD God of hosts: for the children of Israel have forsaken thy covenant, thrown down thine altars, and slain thy prophets with the sword; and I, even I only, am left;

and they seek my life, to take it away. And he said, Go forth, and stand upon the mount before the LORD. And, behold, the LORD passed by, and a great and strong wind rent the mountains, and brake in pieces the rocks before the LORD; but the LORD was not in the wind: and after the wind an earthquake; but the LORD was not in the earthquake: And after the earthquake a fire; but the LORD was not in the fire: and after the fire a still small voice. And it was so, when Elijah heard it, that he wrapped his face in his mantle, and went out, and stood in the entering in of the cave. And, behold, there came a voice unto him, and said, What doest thou here, Elijah? And he said, I have been very jealous for the LORD God of hosts: because the children of Israel have forsaken thy covenant, thrown down thine altars, and slain thy prophets with the sword; and I, even I only, am left; and they seek my life, to take it away. And the LORD said unto him, Go, return on thy way to the wilderness of Damascus: and when thou comest, anoint Hazael to be king over Syria:"— 1 KINGS 19:9–15

A.   God will never __force__ Himself upon you.

B.   God is __always speaking__.

C.   God speaks through __his word__.

D.   God speaks through __our circumstances__

E.   God speaks with His __still small voice within__

F.   God only speaks to __listening hearts__.

G. Listening to God's voice _in your heart_ is different from " _Following your heart_ ."

III. _Feinging_ **prayer to** _Sooth_ **the conscience**

A. It is possible to _fake_ prayer to _sooth the Concience_ .

B. Fake prayer always begins with an _unsurrendured heart_ .

C. Fake prayer will make you _feel beeter rebellion_ .

D. Fake prayer becomes a cover up for _wrong decisions_ .

IV. _____ **about decisions**

A. God is interested in a _____, _____ with you.

B. Prayer is as simple as _____ and _____ toward God.

C. Prayer should begin with _____.

D.   Prayer should continue with _____.

E.   Prayer should continue with _____.

F.   Prayer should conclude with _____.

G.   Consider keeping a _____.

"For God speaketh once, yea twice, yet man perceiveth it not."—JOB 33:14

"And the LORD called Samuel again the third time. And he arose and went to Eli, and said, Here am I; for thou didst call me. And Eli perceived that the LORD had called the child."—I SAMUEL 3:8

Conclusion

_____

_____

Study Questions

1. How do you silence the "voices from without"?

2. How does God speak to His children?

3. What are the characteristics of fake prayer?

4. What are the characteristics of true prayer?

5. List some opportunities you may have in the future that wouldn't necessarily be wrong, but could draw you away from God's will if you're not careful.

6. Why do you think God doesn't just force you to listen to him?

7. Give an illustration of how and why someone might "fake pray" about a decision.

8. Take a moment and write out your own prayer to God regarding your future or a specific decision.

Memory Verse

"Call unto me, and I will answer thee, and show thee great and mighty things, which thou knowest not."—JEREMIAH 33:3

Tight Ropes, Safety Nets, and Stupid People

Step #4—Seek Godly Counsel

Text

"Hear counsel, and receive instruction, that thou mayest be wise in thy latter end. There are many devices in a man's heart; nevertheless the counsel of the LORD, that shall stand."
—PROVERBS 19:20–21

"Every purpose is established by counsel: and with good advice make war."—PROVERBS 20:18

"Blessed is the man that walketh not in the counsel of the ungodly, nor standeth in the way of sinners, nor sitteth in the seat of the scornful."—PSALM 1:1

"Where no counsel is, the people fall: but in the multitude of counsellors there is safety."—PROVERBS 11:14

"Without counsel purposes are disappointed: but in the multitude of counsellors they are established."—PROVERBS 15:22

"The way of a fool is right in his own eyes: but he that hearkeneth unto counsel is wise."—PROVERBS 12:15

"There is no wisdom nor understanding nor counsel against the LORD."—PROVERBS 21:30

Overview

The purpose of this lesson is to help you understand the value and the importance of godly counsel from God-given authorities in your decision-making process. In this lesson, counsel will be compared to a safety net for a tight-rope walker. This is the step that will prevent you from falling into destruction.

Introduction

_____

_____

_____

"There are many devices in a man's heart; nevertheless the counsel of the LORD, that shall stand."—Proverbs 19:21

"Every purpose is established by counsel: and with good advice make war."—Proverbs 20:18

I. What do you do after God ~~Speaks~~ to you?

A. You must ~~Verify~~ God's leading with a ~~multitude of counselors~~.

B. You must ~~know for sure~~ by hearing godly counselors.

II. There are ~~2 types of counsel~~.

"Blessed is the man that walketh not in the counsel of the ungodly, nor standeth in the way of sinners, nor sitteth in the seat of the scornful."—Psalm 1:1

A. Counsel can be ~~ungodly~~.

B. Counsel can be ~~Godly~~.

"That they sent and called him. And Jeroboam and all the congregation of Israel came, and spake unto Rehoboam, saying, Thy father made our yoke grievous: now therefore make thou the grievous service of thy father, and his heavy yoke which he put upon us, lighter, and we will serve thee. And he said unto them, Depart yet for three days, then come again to me. And the people departed. And king Rehoboam consulted with the old men, that stood before Solomon his father while he yet lived, and said, How do ye advise that I may answer this people? And they spake unto him, saying, If thou wilt be a servant unto this people this day, and wilt serve them, and answer them, and speak good words to them, then they will be thy servants for ever. But he forsook the counsel of the old men, which they had given him, and consulted with the young men that were grown up with him, and which stood before him."
—1 KINGS 12:3–8

"And he did evil, because he prepared not his heart to seek the LORD."—2 CHRONICLES 12:14

"But ye have set at nought all my counsel, and would none of my reproof:"—PROVERBS 1:25

III. Why do you _need_ counsel?

A.   The principle of _Confirmation_
"But this thou hast, that thou hatest the deeds of the Nicolaitanes, which I also hate."—REVELATION 2:6

B.   The principle of _God-ordained authority_

"Hast not thou made an hedge about him, and about his house, and about all that he hath on every side? thou hast blessed the work of his hands, and his substance is increased in the land."—JOB 1:10

"He that diggeth a pit shall fall into it; and whoso breaketh an hedge, a serpent shall bite him."—ECCLESIASTES 10:8

(C.) The principle of _Self deception_

IV. How do you _get godly counsel_ ?

A. Refuse to _fahe getting counsel_ .

B. Refuse to _force_ your counselors to _support you_ .

C. Have a _multitude_ of godly counselors.
"Where no counsel is, the people fall: but in the multitude of counsellors there is safety."—PROVERBS 11:14

"Without counsel purposes are disappointed: but in the multitude of counsellors they are established."
—PROVERBS 15:22

D. Listen with an _open heart_ .
"The way of a fool is right in his own eyes: but he that hearkeneth unto counsel is wise."—PROVERBS 12:15

"Hear counsel, and receive instruction, that thou mayest be wise in thy latter end."—PROVERBS 19:20

"Counsel in the heart of man is like deep water; but a man of understanding will draw it out."—PROVERBS 20:5

 E. Look for either <u>confirmation</u> or <u>Contradiction</u> to your decision.

 F. Avoid a "<u>Counsel debate</u>."

V. Don't <u>Defy</u> a multitude of godly counselors.

 A. Don't be afraid to <u>get godly advice</u>.

 B. Don't make a decision if a multitude of counselors are <u>Contradicting</u>.

 C. Wait for God to <u>Confirm</u> through godly counselors.

"The counsel of the LORD standeth for ever, the thoughts of his heart to all generations."—PSALM 33:11

"There is no wisdom nor understanding nor counsel against the LORD."—PROVERBS 21:30

"Hear counsel, and receive instruction, that thou mayest be wise in thy latter end."—PROVERBS 19:20

Conclusion

_____

_____

Study Questions

1. How do you verify God's leading in a decision?

2. List the two types of counsel.

3. Why is getting counsel important?

4. If your counselors are not in agreement regarding a decision, what should you do?

5. If God gives you a direction, why is it so critical that you seek counsel before you make a final decision?

6. List several names of "godly counselors" you can go to when making a decision, and explain why you can trust them.

7. How and why do people fake getting counsel?

8. Describe a time in your life when you made a decision without or against godly counsel and explain why you regret it.

Memory Verse

"The way of a fool is right in his own eyes: but he that hearkeneth unto counsel is wise."—PROVERBS 12:15

Don't Just Stand There; Set That Ship On Fire!

The Testing of a Well-Made Decision

Text

"But none of these things move me, neither count I my life dear unto myself, so that I might finish my course with joy, and the ministry, which I have received of the Lord Jesus, to testify the gospel of the grace of God."—ACTS 20:24

"But he knoweth the way that I take: when he hath tried me, I shall come forth as gold."—JOB 23:10

Overview

This lesson will help you put action to your decision and it will prepare you to expect and overcome the immediate spiritual opposition that your enemy will send.

Introduction

_____

_____

_____

I. <u>Move it or lose it</u> ; it's time for action!

    A. Determine to <u>follow his leading</u>.

    B. Expect the Devil to <u>Challenge you</u>
    <u>   </u>.

"But none of these things move me, neither count I my life dear unto myself, so that I might finish my course with joy, and the ministry, which I have received of the Lord Jesus, to testify the gospel of the grace of God."—ACTS 20:24

    C. Express faith and <u>make your decision</u>.

II. Expect <u>imediate testing</u> of a decision.
"For the gifts and calling of God are without repentance."
—ROMANS 11:29

    A. Every <u>right decision</u> is followed by
    <u>imediate testing</u>.
"For which cause we faint not; but though our outward man perish, yet the inward man is renewed day by day. For our

light affliction, which is but for a moment, worketh for us
a far more exceeding and eternal weight of glory;"
— 2 CORINTHIANS 4:16–17

B. The _____ of your decision will lead
    to _____.

III. What kind of "promised land" is this?

A. God's blessings are more than you can handle.

B. God is preparing you to be strong enough
    for His blessings.

IV. There are three critcal years of testing.

A. You are tested your first year or two of
    college.

B. You are tested your first few years of
    marraige.

C. You are tested your first few years of
    faithfullness to God.

V. How do you _Pass the testing_ of your decision?

A. _Refuse_ to entertain doubts.

B. _renew_ your commitment to God's call.

C. _return_ to Scripture.

D. _remember_ God's promises.

"Nay, in all these things we are more than conquerors through him that loved us."—ROMANS 8:37

"Therefore, my beloved brethren, be ye stedfast, unmoveable, always abounding in the work of the Lord, forasmuch as ye know that your labour is not in vain in the Lord."
—1 CORINTHIANS 15:58

"Therefore seeing we have this ministry, as we have received mercy, we faint not;"—2 CORINTHIANS 4:1

"We are troubled on every side, yet not distressed; we are perplexed, but not in despair; Persecuted, but not forsaken; cast down, but not destroyed;"—2 CORINTHIANS 4:8–9

"Therefore I take pleasure in infirmities, in reproaches, in necessities, in persecutions, in distresses for Christ's sake: for when I am weak, then am I strong."
—2 CORINTHIANS 12:10

"For the which cause I also suffer these things: nevertheless I am not ashamed: for I know whom I have believed, and *am persuaded that he is able to keep that which I have committed unto him against that day."—2 TIMOTHY 1:12*

"Wherefore seeing we also are compassed about with so great a cloud of witnesses, let us lay aside every weight, and the sin which doth so easily beset us, and let us run with patience the race that is set before us, Looking unto Jesus the author and finisher of our faith; who for the joy that was set before him endured the cross, despising the shame, and is set down at the right hand of the throne of God. For consider him that endured such contradiction of sinners against himself, lest ye be wearied and faint in your minds."—HEBREWS 12:1–3

"My brethren, count it all joy when ye fall into divers temptations; Knowing this, that the trying of your faith worketh patience. But let patience have her perfect work, that ye may be perfect and entire, wanting nothing."—JAMES 1:2–4

"Watch ye, stand fast in the faith, quit you like men, be strong."—1 CORINTHIANS 16:13

E. <u>renew</u> your strength in God.
"But he knoweth the way that I take: when he hath tried me, I shall come forth as gold."—JOB 23:10

Conclusion

_____

_____

Study Questions

1. What is every right decision followed by?

2. By testing your decision, what is God preparing you for?

3. List the three critical areas of testing.

4. What are the five steps to passing the testing of your decision?

5. What could happen if you don't intentionally determine to move forward in your decision?

6. What are God's promises to you during the testing of your decision?

7. Why do you think your decisions for college and marriage are so vigorously tested during the beginning years?

8. How can you fail the testing of your decision? What habits could you start developing this week to keep this from happening?

Memory Verse

"Therefore I take pleasure in infirmities, in reproaches, in necessities, in persecutions, in distresses for Christ's sake: for when I am weak, then am I strong."—2 CORINTHIANS 12:10

What Do You Do With a Pet Chicken?

Returning to God's Will from Bad Decisions

Text

"And when they were at Salamis, they preached the word of God in the synagogues of the Jews: and they had also John to their minister."—ACTS 13:5

"And some days after Paul said unto Barnabas, Let us go again and visit our brethren in every city where we have preached the word of the LORD, and see how they do. And Barnabas determined to take with them John, whose surname was Mark. But Paul thought not good to take him with them, who departed from them from Pamphylia, and went not with them to the work. And the contention was so sharp between them, that they departed asunder one from the other: and so Barnabas took Mark, and sailed unto Cyprus;"—ACTS 15:36–39

"Only Luke is with me. Take Mark, and bring him with thee: for he is profitable to me for the ministry."—2 TIMOTHY 4:11

"Brethren, I count not myself to have apprehended: but this one thing I do, forgetting those things which are behind, and reaching forth unto those things which are before, I press toward the mark for the prize of the high calling of God in Christ Jesus."—PHILIPPIANS 3:13–14

"And we know that all things work together for good to them that love God, to them who are the called according to his purpose."—ROMANS 8:28

Overview

This lesson is designed to help you understand God's grace and mercy when it comes to the repenting of bad decisions and undergoing a process of restoration. The lesson will encourage you not to give up when you've made a bad decision, but rather to respond properly to God's leading and to get back on the right track.

Introduction

_____

_____

_____

I. A <u>Second chance</u> in God's will

*"And some days after Paul said unto Barnabas, Let us go again
and visit our brethren in every city where we have preached
the word of the Lord, and see how they do. And Barnabas
determined to take with them John, whose surname was
Mark. But Paul thought not good to take him with them, who
departed from them from Pamphylia, and went not with them
to the work. And the contention was so sharp between them,
that they departed asunder one from the other: and so Barnabas
took Mark, and sailed unto Cyprus;"*—ACTS 15:36–39

   A.   John Mark started serving God <u>faithfully</u>.

   B.   John Mark <u>forsook</u> God's work.

   C.   John Mark <u>returned</u> to God and
        became <u>effective</u> in the ministry.
   *"Only Luke is with me. Take Mark, and bring him with
   thee: for he is profitable to me for the ministry."*
   —2 TIMOTHY 4:11

II. Starting God's perfect will _today_

A. What is _behind_ you cannot be changed.

B. God has _forgotten_ what is behind you.
"Brethren, I count not myself to have apprehended: but this one thing I do, forgetting those things which are behind, and reaching forth unto those things which are before, I press toward the mark for the prize of the high calling of God in Christ Jesus."—PHILIPPIANS 3:13–14

C. God has _future blessings_ if you will follow Him today.

D. Determine to live God's will _from today forward_.

III. _Lingering Damage_ from the "Mistake Zone"

A. Every bad decision has _Bad consequences_.

B. Even bad consequences can be _worked together for good_.
"Likewise the Spirit also helpeth our infirmities: for we know not what we should pray for as we ought: but the Spirit itself maketh intercession for us with groanings which cannot be uttered. And he that searcheth the hearts knoweth what is the mind of the Spirit, because he maketh intercession for the saints according to the will of God. And

*we know that all things work together for good to them
that love God, to them who are the called according to his
purpose."*—ROMANS 8:26–28

IV. A window of <u>reversal</u>

*"Or despisest thou the riches of his goodness and forbearance and
longsuffering; not knowing that the goodness of God leadeth
thee to repentance?"*—ROMANS 2:4

A. Many bad decisions <u>can't be undone</u>.

B. Many bad decisions <u>can be undone</u>.

C. Don't be <u>too proud</u> to undo a bad
decision <u>before its too late</u>.

*"And the word of the LORD came unto Jonah the second
time..."*—JONAH 3:1A

*"He saith to him again the second time, Simon, son of Jonas,
lovest thou me?"*—JOHN 21:16A

Conclusion

_____

_____

Study Questions

1. When does God's perfect will start?

2. How does God deal with your bad decisions?

3. What is the "window of reversal"?

4. What sin can keep you from reversing your bad decisions?

5. How can your past mistakes help you in the future?

6. List three "bad decisions" that cannot be undone and explain why it is crucial to seek out God's perfect will, even after these decisions are made.

7. Why is it dangerous to dwell on past mistakes?

8. Choose two characters in the Bible who made bad decisions. Explain how their bad decisions hurt them but also how God was able to use them after they turned back to Him.

Memory Verse

"Brethren, I count not myself to have apprehended: but this one thing I do, forgetting those things which are behind, and reaching forth unto those things which are before, I press toward the mark for the prize of the high calling of God in Christ Jesus."—Philippians 3:13–14

Hey, Dad, What's Tomorrow?

Understanding God's Call on Every Believer

Text

"Who hath saved us, and called us with an holy calling, not according to our works, but according to his own purpose and grace, which was given us in Christ Jesus before the world began,"—2 TIMOTHY 1:9

"But as he which hath called you is holy, so be ye holy in all manner of conversation,"—1 PETER 1:15

"But ye are a chosen generation, a royal priesthood, an holy nation, a peculiar people; that ye should shew forth the praises of him who hath called you out of darkness into his marvellous light:"—1 PETER 2:9

"But as God hath distributed to every man, as the Lord hath called every one, so let him walk. And so ordain I in all churches."—1 CORINTHIANS 7:17

"That ye would walk worthy of God, who hath called you unto his kingdom and glory."—1 THESSALONIANS 2:12

"Fight the good fight of faith, lay hold on eternal life, whereunto thou art also called, and hast professed a good profession before many witnesses."—1 TIMOTHY 6:12

"But as it is written, Eye hath not seen, nor ear heard, neither have entered into the heart of man, the things which God hath prepared for them that love him."—1 CORINTHIANS 2:9

Overview

This lesson is designed to help you understand God's call on your life. Regardless of what you do for a living, you are called to live for God and to surrender your whole life for his purposes. This lesson will challenge you to consider a call to ministry, but more importantly to surrender to God's call to live for Christ alone.

Introduction

_____

_____

_____

I. ~~First things~~ **first.**

"Who hath saved us, and **called us with an holy calling**, not according to our works, but according to his own purpose and grace, which was given us in Christ Jesus before the world began,"—2 TIMOTHY 1:9

"But as he which **hath called you** is holy, so be ye holy in all manner of conversation;"—1 PETER 1:15

"But ye are a chosen generation, a royal priesthood, an holy nation, a peculiar people; that ye should shew forth the praises of him **who hath called you** out of darkness into his marvelous light:"—1 PETER 2:9

"For even hereunto **were ye called**: because Christ also suffered for us, leaving us an example, that ye should follow his steps:"—1 PETER 2:21

"Among whom are **ye also the called of Jesus Christ**: To all that be in Rome, beloved of God, **called to be saints**: Grace to you and peace from God our Father, and the Lord Jesus Christ."—ROMANS 1:6–7

"And we know that all things work together for good to them that love God, to them who are the **called according to his purpose**."—ROMANS 8:28

*"Moreover whom he did predestinate, **them he also called**: and whom he called, them he also justified: and whom he justified, them he also glorified."*—ROMANS 8:30

*"God is faithful, by whom **ye were called** unto the fellowship of his Son Jesus Christ our Lord."*—1 CORINTHIANS 1:9

*"But as God hath distributed to every man, as the **Lord hath called every one**, so let him walk."*—1 CORINTHIANS 7:17A

*"I therefore, the prisoner of the Lord, beseech you that ye walk worthy of the vocation **wherewith ye are called**,"* ′
—EPHESIANS 4:1

*"That ye would walk worthy of God, **who hath called you** unto his kingdom and glory."*—1 THESSALONIANS 2:12

*"Fight the good fight of faith, lay hold on eternal life, **whereunto thou art also called**, and hast professed a good profession before many witnesses."*—1 TIMOTHY 6:12

- A.   You are called to <u>live for God</u>.

- B.   You are called to <u>serve God</u> regardless of your vocation.

- C.   <u>full surrender to God</u> to God is our reasonable service.

II. Is God calling you into <u>ministry</u>?

- A.   A ministry call is not always a <u>momentous experience</u>.

B. A ministry call is often a process of _growth_ _and realization_ as you follow God.

C. God accepts _____ into His service.

III. There's no place like _God's will_.

A. Serving in full-time ministry often gets a _bad rep_.

B. Serving in full-time ministry deserves the same _Consideration_ as any other vocation.

C. Let _God be God_, and you will never regret following Him.

"For ye have not received the spirit of bondage again to fear; but ye have received the Spirit of adoption, whereby we cry, **Abba***, Father."*—ROMANS 8:15

"...as the Lord hath called every one, so let him walk." —1 CORINTHIANS 7:17B

Conclusion

_____

_____

Study Questions

1. Whether or not you're called to full-time ministry, what is every Christian called to do?

2. What is your "reasonable service" to God?

3. What process is often involved in God's calling to ministry?

4. What kind of consideration should be given to full-time ministry?

5. List some basic ways that every Christian can serve God.

6. In what areas of your "reasonable service" to God do you need to grow the most in? What can you do to improve in these areas?

7. What are some false ideas people get about full-time ministry?

8. How can you let God be God in your life?

Memory Verse

"I beseech you therefore, brethren, by the mercies of God, that ye present your bodies a living sacrifice, holy, acceptable unto God, which is your reasonable service. And be not conformed to this world: but be ye transformed by the renewing of your mind, that ye may prove what is that good, and acceptable, and perfect, will of God."—ROMANS 12:1–2

For additional Christian
growth resources visit
www.strivingtogether.com